THE NEW WORLD

OF CONSTRUCTION

ENGINEERING

Steel cables radiate from the inner tension ring to outer compression ring in the suspended roof of Madison Square Garden in New York.

THE
NEW WORLD
OF CONSTRUCTION
ENGINEERING

By GEORGE SULLIVAN

Illustrated with photographs

DODD, MEAD & COMPANY, NEW YORK

PICTURE CREDITS

Association of American Railroads, 11; Australian News and Information Bureau, 73; Bay Area Rapid Transit District, 48, 51, 52; Bethlehem Steel Corporation, 2, 16, 17, 45, 46; Bureau of Public Roads, 39; Bureau of Reclamation, A. E. Turner, 44, 59; Caterpillar Tractor Company, 35; Chesapeake Bay Bridge and Tunnel Authority, 43; *Civil Engineering*, 13, 33, 41; David R. Graham & Associates, Consulting Engineers, 18; Expo 67, 19; Federal Aviation Agency, 63, 64; Grumman Aircraft Engineering Corporation, 78; Marietta Concrete Company, 21; McDowell-Wellman Engineering Company, 57 (bottom); NASA, 75, 77; Netherlands Information Agency, 72; New York Public Library, 10; Parsons, Brinckerhoff, Quade & Douglas, 49, 65, 70; The Port of New York Authority, 27, 29, 66; State of California, Department of Highways, 37; State of California, Department of Water Resources, 54, 57 (top); Steel Products News Bureau, 23; Tishman Construction Company, 31; Triborough Bridge and Tunnel Authority, 8; Westinghouse, 60.

ACKNOWLEDGMENTS

Countless people provided source material and photographs for this book, and it would be impossible to name them all. But special thanks are due the following: Stanley Metalitz, Office of Research & Development, Federal Highway Administration; R. Dan Mahaney, Airport Manager, Dulles International Airport; E. B. Markow and Ralph Frei, Grumman Aircraft Engineering Corporation; Max L. Brown, Bethlehem Steel Corporation; Anthony Mavis of Parsons, Brinckerhoff, Quade and Douglas; Leon Katz, The Port of New York Authority; Mylene Coonen, Netherlands Information Agency; Julian Scheer, National Aeronautics and Space Administration; Herb Hands, Public Information Officer, American Society of Civil Engineers, and Hal Hunt, Editor, *Civil Engineering*. I am especially grateful to Mary E. Jessup, News Editor, *Civil Engineering*, who checked the manuscript for technical accuracy. Information concerning skyscrapers of the future is from a survey compiled by Julien J. Studley, Inc., New York City.

Contents

The Verrazano-Narrows Bridge rates as a miracle of modern engineering.

1 Building a Better World

On a clear, wind-snapped day early in November, 1825, New York's Governor DeWitt Clinton, standing in the bow of a gaily decorated canalboat, slowly poured a keg of water brought from Lake Erie into New York Harbor. This symbolic act officially opened the Erie Canal, a mighty waterway linking the Hudson River and the Great Lakes. Cannons boomed; crowds paraded.

The Erie and Barge Canal came to have a powerful effect upon commerce of the day. Before the waterway was built, Philadelphia ranked as the country's number one seaport. But the canal, by making New York City the gateway to the vast interior of the country, quickly made that city pre-eminent. And New York was not the only city to benefit. The canal carried an enormous amount of boat and barge traffic, and towns all along its course—Albany, Utica, Syracuse, Rochester, and Buffalo—developed rapidly.

The construction of the Erie Canal was even more signifi-cant for the impact that it had on civil engineering in the

The "marriage of waters" signaled the opening of the Erie Canal.

United States. In 1817, the year construction began, America had very few engineers. The men who built the Erie Canal were clever and resourceful farmers, lawyers, businessmen, and surveyors. They penetrated 363 miles of forested wilderness without excavating or earth-moving machines. At the beginning, they had merely the shovel, pick, wheelbarrow, and wagon for equipment. Their most sophisticated instrument was the level.

Work along the canal route was divided into sections, and local residents, with horse- or ox-drawn plows and scrapers, dug the canal bed. They learned to use mortar, a mixture of sand, lime and water, to bind stone to stone. They learned to hoist heavy objects, using ropes and pulley blocks. They learned to haul and lift by means of the wheeled windlass. They taught themselves to be engineers. The Erie Canal has rightly been called the First American Engineering School.

Once the construction of the canal was completed, and its success established, the building of other canals quickly followed. The Pennsylvania Canal came next, and then the Alle-

10

gheny Portage, a waterway which enabled canalboats to "leap" the Allegheny Mountains.

America's canal era was short-lived, however. Though canal building served as a great training ground for American engineers, the emphasis throughout most of the nineteenth century was on railroad construction. In 1827 the Baltimore and Ohio Railroad was incorporated. By 1858 it had 358 miles of track and had established itself as the most notable of our pioneer railroads. The continent was crossed in 1869, but the greatest decade of railroad construction was from 1880-1890. Over 70,000 miles of new track were laid.

Railroad building taught Americans how to roll iron shapes and rails. And it did more. It ushered in an era of dramatic bridge construction. The truss bridge, with its uncomplicated iron framework, was introduced in 1847. Longer and stronger spans followed. John Roebling showed the practicality of the suspension principle in bridge building with a double-deck span over the Niagara River gorge. Captain James Buchanan Eads, using the arch, created a masterpiece in the St. Louis

Railroad construction, along with canal building, helped to school generations of American engineers. This wooden trestle was located near Grangerville, Idaho.

Bridge of 1874, a structure that opened up great horizons for a wondrous new metal—steel. Roebling's monumental achievement was the Brooklyn Bridge, a suspension span opened in 1883.

Greater projects followed. The twentieth century saw the construction of the Hoover Dam, the world's highest; the Empire State Building, the world's tallest; and the Panama Canal, the cut that linked two oceans. But the canal builders and railroad pioneers of the nineteenth century paved the way for these and all other modern engineering wonders.

What is to come is even more amazing. Tomorrow's engineers will be called upon to master new frontiers beneath the sea, on the moon, and in the farthest reaches of space.

Buildings, bridges, and dams; harbors, tunnels, and airports; waterways, railways, and highways; water power and water supply—all of these are the domain of the construction engineer, or, more properly, the *civil* engineer. The word "civil" is Latin in origin; it means "citizen." And citizens—of a city, a state, or a nation—are the foremost concern of the civil engineer.

Engineering is as old as recorded history and engineers of the ancient past were responsible for structures every bit as marvelous as those being built today. The pyramids of Egypt, the Hanging Gardens of Babylon, the Temple of Diana at Ephesus, and the Pharos of Alexandria were all structures which required an immense degree of engineering skill in their design and construction. Without engineers, the Chinese could not have constructed the Great Wall or the Grand Canal. In Central America, engineers among the Mayans built remarkable temples and palaces.

The engineering accomplishments of ancient Rome were so extraordinary that they were not surpassed until the nineteenth century. Buildings, roads, bridges, and water supply systems for more than 200 communities were scattered over the Empire. In the later stages of Roman history, the *architectus*, or master builder, emerged. He used the arch as the basis for his bridges and aqueducts. He developed construction machines—the treadmill hoist and the pile driver. He developed cement—a true hydraulic cement—made of volcanic ash and lime, which hardened into a stonelike mass. It was the best cement available for more than 1,500 years.

The Middle Ages were notable for the castle, the fortress-home, with its massive walls and great chief tower, or *donjon*. Castles were built mainly in France, but also in England and Germany. The engineer of the day was largely a military engineer, a man who made the "engines" of war—the battering ram and the catapult for hurling stones and similar missiles.

The cathedrals of the Middle Ages remain as "man's greatest achievement in stonemasonry," said the late James Kip Finch, the noted engineering historian. (Stone today has no structural purpose; it is merely a surfacing material.) Cathedral construction featured arched stone frames, step roofs, thin walls, and stained glass windows.

France was the foremost country in engineering during the

Bridge building of the nineteenth century reached its zenith with the construction of the Brooklyn Bridge, opened in 1883.

seventeenth and eighteenth centuries. Bridges, roads and canals were the order of the day. Many advances were achieved. Surveying devices grew more sophisticated. Drafting instruments, such as the ruler, compass, and protractor, were developed. Progress continued uninterrupted until the Napoleonic Wars.

Britain lagged behind most of the rest of Europe in the development of engineering skills. However, in 1750, an Englishman, one John Smeaton, was the first to describe himself as a "civil engineer." He did so in an effort to distinguish his calling from that of the architect or the military engineer. The son of a lawyer, Smeaton is most noted for his design of the Eddystone Lighthouse. It was circular and of decreasing diameter from the base, not simply cylinder-shaped. Located on the Eddystone Rocks off the coast of Cornwall, it stood for more than a century.

Industry and engineering in England developed together to transform the country from an agricultural nation to an industrial one. At the close of the reign of Queen Elizabeth, railroads crisscrossed the nation. Steam power and machines led to the founding of virtually every type of industry. The British showed the way in bridge building, tunnel construction, and in the development of subway transportation. England developed the "Bessemer process," the blast furnace method of making steel.

"Engineering came of age in twentieth-century America," said James Kip Finch. Steam, electric, and gas power replaced hand labor. Chemistry and metallurgy (the science of metals) triggered the development of a whole new world of construction materials.

Engineering advances of the past 100 years completely revolutionized the world in which we live. In the future they promise to do the same.

2 Some Old Ideas with a New Twist

"The public doesn't require any new ideas," Henrik Ibsen, the Norwegian dramatist and poet, once observed. "The public is best served by good, old-fashioned ideas it already has." Some modern trends in construction engineering bear out this observation.

The new Madison Square Garden Sports and Entertainment Center in New York City, which opened in 1968, has 20,234 seats, and not one is blocked by a pillar. There are no pillars—thanks to the building's cable-supported roof.

This unique drum-shaped structure is one of an increasing number of buildings to use a suspension roof. Since 1960 at least 30 buildings in the United States have been covered in this manner. Does this represent a new concept in structural design? Not at all. It is simply a modern treatment of an age-old idea. In A.D. 80 the Romans employed the suspension roof principle in building a sunshade for the Colosseum.

Pancake-flat and circular, the suspended roof of Madison Square Garden has a diameter of 404 feet. Engineers say it is one of the largest roofs of its type in the country, possibly in the world. It has three basic parts: an inner tension ring, an outer compression ring, which rims the top perimeter of the structure, and steel cables—48 of them—strung between the two rings. This arrangement of parts is very much like the wheel of a bicycle, essentially a system of spokes connecting an inner ring with an outer one.

Each one of the steel cables is "spun" from 271 individual wires. The cables are 3¾ inches in diameter, about the size of a man's arm. They have a total weight of 163 tons. They support not only a steel deck and the concrete roof, but two additional floors—1,000 tons in all. The added floors are used for lighting and mechanical equipment.

Each cable is linked to the tension ring by a special socket. These are huge, each weighing 659 pounds. The sockets that connect the cable to the outer ring are only slightly smaller. The tension ring, with its welded plates radiating from the center, looks like a great steel sunburst. It is 40 feet in diameter; it weighs 105 tons.

Welded inner tension ring used in the construction of the suspended roof of Madison Square Garden looks like a steel sunburst.

Steel cable used in the Madison Square Garden roof system is as thick as a man's arm. Sockets weigh 659 pounds each.

In assembling the roof, the tension ring was hoisted to the top of a temporary steel tower. The cables were strung and tightened. Then the steel tower was taken away. The ring floated free. Today spectators can see the tension ring and the cables radiating from it directly over the arena floor.

Cable can be used in two ways to hold up a roof system. The roof can be supported directly by the cables, as is the case at Madison Square Garden Center, or the cables can support structural steel parts which, in turn, bear the roof load. This latter technique was used in the Tulsa Exhibition Center, which opened in 1967. A ten-acre structure, it has the world's largest cable-supported roof. (Madison Square Garden has the largest *circular* roof.)

Eighty-two tapered steel masts, each 80 feet tall, are a key feature in the Tulsa building. Strong steel cables have been strung over the tops of these masts to act like great suspenders. They attach to long steel girders which support the roof.

The result is that three-quarters of the inner floor space of

17

the exhibition hall is free of pillars. (The mast bottoms intrude at the edges of the structure.) Exhibitors have almost half a million square feet of display space. "It's so spacious," says one, "it's almost like having a roofed-over Rhode Island."

Many of the more than thirty million people who visited Expo 67 in Montreal found the fascinating exhibit to be Habitat, a unique experiment in housing design. To the eye, Habitat appears as a cluster of pyramided and jutting concrete boxes. The boxes form dwelling units of one to four rooms in size.

Habitat was paid for by the Canadian government and designed by Moshe Safdie, a twenty-eight-year-old architect from Israel. He conceived the idea of stacking the boxes in such a way that the roof of one forms a garden terrace for the dwelling unit above. Tenants have a striking view of the Montreal skyline across the St. Lawrence River.

Habitat, now a permanent fixture in Montreal, contains 158 housing units and reaches a height of 12 floors. There are pedestrian streets at the sixth and tenth floor levels. An enormous artistic success (although its tremendous cost has held back the construction of other such projects), it has been said that ". . . the promise of the future is in this housing."

Tulsa Exhibition Center has a suspended roof which covers a ten-acre area.

Habitat was judged a fascinating experiment in housing design at Expo 67.

But the concept expressed at Habitat is not unique. Five centuries ago the Zuni, Hopi, and Shoshoni Indians, who inhabited the semi-desert regions that are now parts of the states of Arizona and New Mexico, lived in tiered dwellings very similar to those displayed at Expo 67. Theirs were sandstone-walled, roofed with brush grass and adobe mud. They were arranged so that the roof of the lower unit formed the means of access as well as the front yard of the unit above. These Indian tribes placed their clustered dwellings on lofty mesas or level plains, or sometimes cut them into the rocky walls of cliffs or canyons.

While the basic idea of Habitat may be reminiscent of that used by a previous civilization, the construction techniques were thoroughly modern. The concrete boxes that go to make up Habitat are all the same size. Each measures 17.5 by 38.5 feet, and is 10 feet high. By using the same measurements for every box, the builder was able to mass-produce the walls by simple precasting methods. The roofs were cast separately. After each box was assembled, it was fitted with molded plastic bathroom and kitchen units. Then the box, which weighed 80 tons, was hoisted into place by a huge derrick. It took 11 months to complete construction.

Up until the last decade of the nineteenth century, building walls did what they seemed intended to do—hold up buildings. But as structures increased in height, this concept made for buildings that were extremely bulky and space-consuming. The 16-story Monadnock Building, erected in Chicago in the early 1880's, had walls that were five feet thick.

Steel-frame construction put an end to this problem. The Home Insurance Company Building in Chicago, started in 1883, was the first to demonstrate the practicality of the steel skeleton. Walls could be as thin as curtains. In fact, they were, and are, called "curtain walls." Curtain-wall construction is expressed in virtually every skyscraper ever built, including the "Queen of Skyscrapers," the Empire State Building.

Today there is a trend backward—toward the use of walls that enclose the building's floors and support the structure as well. However, today's load-bearing walls do not have to be fortress-thick. Advances in the manufacture of concrete have made this material ideal for load-bearing walls. Wall panels are precast at a cement plant, then delivered to the building site and hoisted into place. Modern cranes and derricks, which are able to lift incredible loads, make it possible to handle the heavy precast panels.

The headquarters building of the American Bible Society in New York City, completed in 1966, and 12 stories tall, was one of the first modern structures to use the "bearing-wall" technique with structural precast sections. This method of construction provides clear space within the building from wall to wall without obstruction.

The American Bible Society building was followed by the Huntington Trust Company building in Columbus, Ohio, also 12 stories. Wall sections for the Columbus building were produced in wood-frame molds lined with fiber glass. Steel reinforcing rods were placed in the molds first. Then the concrete was poured in. In 18 hours the casting was hard enough to be

One of the precast panels used in the Huntington Trust Company building in Columbus, Ohio.

removed from the mold. For the Huntington Trust structure, each wall section was 24 feet long and 12 feet high. Each weighed 18 tons, yet the castings did not vary in size by more than one-eighth of an inch.

Two tower cranes, each operating from the interior of the building, raised the wall sections into place. One section was placed atop another and then the two were bolted together. After all the panels on one floor level were erected, the floor itself was constructed.

The color of such buildings can be varied by varying the color of the cement and the type of small pebbles or stone used in the mix. In the American Bible Society building the cement is white and the small stones are off-white.

Norfolk, Kansas City, and New Orleans are cities where other buildings have recently been constructed using structural precast panels. Steel can also be used in this type of construction. The most notable examples of load-bearing walls of steel are the twin towers of the World Trade Center in New York City.

The arch is one of engineering's basic pieces of design. Arches are used as the means of support above an open space, as in a doorway or a window, or over a highway or a river gorge. Arches can be built of stone, brick, timber, steel, aluminum, or reinforced concrete. Their use dates to the most ancient of times. Bridges are traditionally cited as the best examples of arch-type construction.

Today, however, the most glorious of them all is a soaring giant of an arch recently completed in St. Louis. Anchored in the bedrock along the shore of the Mississippi River, and known as the Gateway Arch, it is a masterpiece of stainless steel that dominates the St. Louis skyline and seems destined to become one of the most noted structures in the United States, if not the world.

The Gateway Arch is a free-standing monument, not the structural basis for a bridge or a building's roof. It is 630 feet high, the largest arch in the world. It is the second tallest monument, exceeded only by the Eiffel Tower in Paris. It serves as the centerpiece of an 82-acre park, officially known as the Jefferson National Expansion Memorial. This name refers to President Jefferson's negotiation of the Louisiana Purchase in 1803, and to the great surge of frontiersmen who passed through St. Louis to settle the new lands.

Engineers call the Gateway Arch an "inverted catenary." A catenary is the curve that a chain or a cord takes when hung freely between two points at the same level. From a structural standpoint this is the soundest arch of all. Thrust passes downward through the legs to be absorbed by the foundations.

Each leg of the Gateway Arch has been anchored in 12,000 tons of concrete. These foundations are triangular in shape, 90 feet on each side. They were sunk 45 feet into the bedrock.

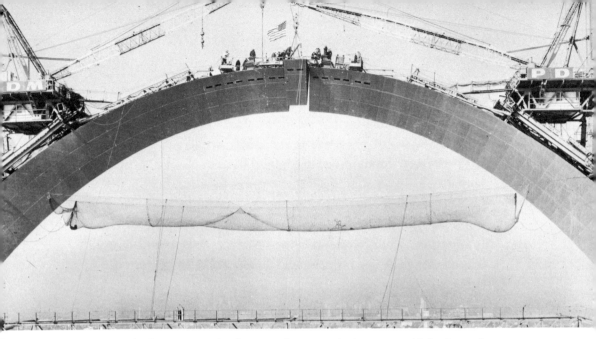

Inserting the keystone in the St. Louis Gateway Arch was a ticklish piece of work. Note "creeper" cranes.

The Gateway Arch ranks as a stunning monument. Made of gleaming stainless steel, it is 630 feet in height.

The arch itself was built of huge preassembled triangular sections of double-walled stainless steel. After a section was hoisted and welded into place, its double-walled skin was filled with concrete. Steel rods were added to increase the structure's strength.

It is usual for arches to be built over "falsework," a temporary scaffolding of wood or steel which supports the structure until construction has been completed. But a different method was used in building the Gateway Arch. Twin "creeper" cranes, riding on tracks mounted on each leg of the arch, hoisted each section into place.

In the construction of any arch, the most critical phase is placing the keystone, the central and topmost piece of the structure. Setting the keystone in the Gateway Arch, so as to make a single unit of the two curving legs, was especially ticklish. This keystone weighed twelve tons. About 10,000 people gathered on the river bank to watch the placement. Workmen atop the structure noticed that the sun's rays were causing the steel skin of the arch to expand, thereby narrowing the gap into which the keystone was to be placed. Fire hoses pumped water over the steel to cool it. Then the keystone was lowered into place by one of the creeper derricks.

The Gateway Arch is not only a monument, it is an observation point as well. Its hollow legs contain curving elevator shafts. Small cable cars carry visitors to the very top of the arch where there is an observation chamber. It is a four-minute ride. Visiting the top is an unforgettable experience; the view is spectacular. On a day when a strong wind is blowing, the arch has a slight sway. This is normal, though. It has been built to withstand winds of up to 150 mph.

3 Superskyscrapers

The office building of the 1990's will be a soaring giant, rising 100 stories or more. It will stand on an enormous plot of ground, one made possible by closing down several city streets in the area and merging into one the various parcels of land in between.

When tenants move in, they will find furniture and furnishings already there. Desks and chairs will be made of plastic, and premolded in place. Carpeting and flooring materials will be sprayed on. High-speed pneumatic elevators will whisk workers to their floors. A moving corridor will glide them to their offices.

Partitions between working spaces will be a thing of the past. Better sound control will enable individuals to work in open areas. When partitions are necessary, they will be made of plastic and curved or angled so as to be more appealing to the eye.

Superskyscrapers will boast recreation facilities and lounge areas for workers, and cafeterias and restaurants. Lights will never have to be turned on or turned off. Instead, entire ceilings will be perpetual light sources, with the amount of artificial light automatically controlled by the amount of natural light, whether it be night or day. There will be no bulbs to change.

The building's air-conditioning system will render the interior dust-free. All paper waste will be speedily gotten rid of by a vacuum-powered tube disposal system. A man may never see his secretary. To dictate a letter, he will simply "plug in" to a central stenographic system.

This is how officers of leading corporations describe the office building of tomorrow. But such "dream" buildings may be a reality much sooner than anyone expects.

The best evidence of this is the World Trade Center in New York City, which will bring together men and corporations engaged in world trade. The principal feature of the World Trade Center is a pair of tremendous steel towers, each 110 stories, 1,350 feet tall. No buildings on earth are taller.

These matched towers assign New York City's Empire State Building to mere second place among the world's tallest structures. Built in 1931, the Empire State Building is "only" 102 stories, 1,250 feet in height.

For decades after the completion of the Empire State, no one believed that a building as tall or taller would ever be built again—for two reasons. So many workers used the building that they jammed city streets and clogged transportation facilities in the area. Laws were passed to limit the size of a building to one-quarter of the area of the lot on which it was to stand. Buildings of the 1940's and 1950's seldom rose more than fifty or sixty stories as a result.

In addition, the Empire State Building was not a financial success for its original owners. A great deal of space which, in an ordinary building, would have been used for offices and rented, had to be given over to elevator shafts. Elevators do not bring in any rent.

Both of these problems were solved in planning the World Trade Center. The towers were not limited to a single city

Twin towers of the World Trade Center are each 110 stories, the tallest structure in the world.

block or even a pair of them. Instead they rise from a super-block, a 16-acre "lot" which was made possible by closing the streets of fourteen small city blocks.

Engineers overcame the problem of space-using elevators by installing two "sky lobbies"—on the 41st floor and 74th floor of each tower. Passengers take express cars to these floors. Then they transfer to "local" elevators which make stops at all floors above. Local elevators also serve the second to the 40th floor, but huge banks of elevator shafts running the entire height of the building are not needed.

Anyone who has ever seen a skyscraper being built knows that it gets its support from an internal skeleton of steel or concrete beams. The outer walls are hung like curtains upon this framework. But the Trade Center towers are different. They have no interior columns. Instead, they get their supporting strength from a series of exterior columns which are spaced 3¼ feet apart. Like giant straight steel ribs, they run from the very top of each structure into the foundation. They support the floors and frame the narrow windows. New and stronger types of steel make this method of construction possible.

This framing system, which renders interior floors of the towers as column-free as a football field, presented many new and unique problems in structural design. An army of engineers was called upon to help in the planning. Said one of them: "We could have built the towers out of paper just by using all the plans and working drawings that have gone into this thing."

Like all of New York City's skyscrapers, the towers of the World Trade Center are supported by a flaky, gray crystal-flecked rock called "schist." It lies about 70 feet below the surface of the ground. Before construction could begin, engineers had to dig what they called "a giant empty bathtub," actually a watertight hole that covered an area of eight city blocks. The bottom of the hole was Manhattan schist—the bedrock. The foundations for the towers were driven into the rock.

Before the immense hole could be dug, an underground wall of concrete, three feet thick, had to be built around the edges. The wall reached from the surface of the ground to the bedrock. Its purpose was to hold back water seepage from the nearby Hudson River. Without the wall, the big hole would have become a small lake.

A crane lowers a cage of reinforcing steel into the foundation trench of the World Trade Center.

Engineers used a unique construction method to build the wall. First, a narrow trench was dug down to the bedrock. Heavy steel bits broke up the rocks and other obstructions. Clamshell buckets removed the soil and debris. As soon as the soil was removed from the trench, it was replaced by a pudding-thick mixture of powdered clay and water. Called "slurry," this material held up the walls of the trench and prevented water from seeping in. Then concrete was piped through the slurry into the bottom of the trench. As the concrete filled the trench, the slurry was forced to the top and skimmed off. The pouring of concrete continued until all of the slurry was forced out of the trench. The engineers had their wall as soon as the concrete hardened.

Not everyone applauds the World Trade Center, not by any means. It has been condemned for its bigness, and called "the world's tallest fiasco." Bird lovers have protested that the tower buildings will be a serious menace to night-flying birds.

It has been said that the towers will create interference with television reception in New York City, adjacent New Jersey, and nearby Connecticut. Some people claim that the pair of flat-topped giants will destroy the beauty of Manhattan's inspiring skyline. Such critics fail to realize that many of the structures that make up that skyline were attacked too. The first of New York's tall buildings were called "senseless" and "barbaric" by people of an earlier day.

Chicago is another city that has seen its skyline sharply changed recently. The structure is a single tower, the 100-story John Hancock Center. In 1968, when steelwork reached its highest point, the structure ranked second only to the Empire State Building in height.

The twin towers of the World Trade Center in New York City gain their structural strength from steel columns in the exterior walls, but the John Hancock building relies upon a totally different structural system. Five huge X-shaped crossbars, each one several stories high, straddle each of the four sides of the tower to provide structural support. The tower is 1,107 feet tall. It is not sheer, but gently tapered—"like a square candle," says one engineer.

When the project was originally planned, it was to consist of two separate towers, a 70-story apartment building and a 45-story office building. But the two-tower plan would have covered too great a portion of the building site. Someone suggested putting the smaller tower on top of the larger one. Not many years ago such a suggestion would have been laughed at. But now, thanks to high-strength steels and new engineering techniques, the idea is practical.

Thus the John Hancock Center is both an office building and an apartment building. Offices occupy the 13th through the 41st stories. A 48-floor apartment house begins on the 45th floor and stretches to the 92nd floor. These are the highest apartments in the world.

Chicago's John Hancock Center towers 100 stories.

Above the apartment area, floors are given over to restaurants, lounges, and an observation area. A two-level lobby on the 44th and 45th floors furnishes residents with shops, lounges, and a swimming pool. A large courtyard at the base is a reflecting pool in the summer, and an ice-skating rink in the winter.

The 1990's are already here!

31

4 Coast to Coast — Nonstop

The United States is in the midst of an enormous road-building program. It is the greatest single construction project the world has ever known. It is taking our best engineering brains, the latest construction techniques, and the finest materials. In 1972, when it is completed, the benefits of the project will be felt by every citizen.

It is difficult to comprehend the immense size of this program, but consider these statistics:

In total, 41,000 miles of highway are to be constructed; 84 per cent of them are four lanes, which translates into 170,000 "lane miles" of highway. Or look at it this way: Enough concrete is being used to build six sidewalks to the moon.

In rural areas the average cost per mile is $639,000. In cities, where land is more expensive and construction problems are greater, the cost is $3.6 million per mile. The total cost of the program is $41 billion.

The system will have 12,000 interchanges, 22,000 highway and grade separations and 13,000 bridges.

The Interstate System will have 12,000 interchanges and 13,000 bridges. This scene is near Detroit.

The necessary excavating will move enough material to bury the entire state of Connecticut knee-deep in dirt.

Highway design and construction for this National System of Interstate and Defense Highways, must follow rigid standards. Safety features are being built in. One-way strips of pavement must be at least three lanes wide. A median strip dividing the highway—often a planted area—must be included. There can be no traffic lights, intersections, railroad crossings, steep grades, or sharp curves. Wide shoulders have to be provided for emergency stops. Motorists of the 1970's will drive on a nationwide nonstop boulevard.

A shield-shaped red, white, and blue sign indicates an Interstate Highway. Each highway is numbered; long roads have double numbers. If the number is even—10 to 90—the highway runs east and west. If the number is odd—5 to 95—it runs north and south.

A striking feature of modern highways is the way in which

33

they are designed. Engineers now use computers. Problems of road layout and interchange design that once took weeks to solve can now be unraveled in a matter of minutes.

After the highway has been planned and designed, and once the necessary land has been acquired, the contractor starts moving men and machines to the site. Modern earth-moving machines can literally move mountains. First come the bulldozers, ripping and scraping, clearing away trees, boulders, and buildings—anything that stands in the right of way. Then giant tractor-scrapers go to work, transporting tons of earth to level the hills and fill the valleys. Motor graders, each with a giant curved blade, do the final leveling. Last come the mobile cranes. They lay drain pipes beneath the roadway to carry off water.

As soon as the roadway has been graded, construction crews begin building the sub-base, the underlying part of the highway that motorists never see. The sub-base acts to support the pavement and protect it from moisture from below. It is composed of sand, gravel, crushed stone, or slag, a waste material produced in the manufacture of steel. Trucks dump the sub-base material into a spreading machine. After it has been spread it is firmly packed with flat-wheel or rubber-tire rollers. Sometimes vibrating tamping machines are used.

Now the highway is ready to be paved. Engineers can choose from one of two paving materials: portland cement or asphalt.

Portland cement is a type of concrete, and the most widely used of all modern construction materials. It is made by burning a mixture of limestone, clay, and a variety of mineral substances, and then grinding these into a fine powder. When portland cement is mixed with the proper amounts of water, sand, and small stones or gravel, it forms a paste which hardens into a strong, rocklike mass. About 60 per cent of the country's highways are made of portland cement.

In highway building, giant bulldozers lead the parade of construction equipment.

Tractor scrapers (above) level the hills and fill the valleys. Motor graders (below) do the final leveling.

Asphalt, sometimes called the world's oldest engineering material—Noah is said to have used asphalt to waterproof the Ark—is a liquid that is obtained from petroleum. It is blended with crushed rock, stone, or slag. This mix, when laid in layers and firmly packed, forms a rugged, flexible pavement.

Engineering opinions differ as to which of these two materials is the better. Asphalt, because it is more flexible than concrete, is usually preferred wherever the roadway is expected to settle. It is also used on city streets because it is easier to patch. In some areas of the country, the sand and stone available are not suitable for making asphalt pavements. This is true in the Midwest principally, so Midwestern highways are usually made of concrete.

No matter which of the two materials is used, the method of paving is completely automated. It is almost a push-button operation.

Contractors and engineers agree that the greatest advance in concrete paving in recent years is the "slip-form paver." This machine, which operates astride the leveled roadbed, does everything but install the highway signs. Moving forward steadily, it spreads the concrete, packs it down, and finishes it to the desired degree of smoothness. It can lay 8 to 10 feet of concrete in one minute. Only one operator is required. Until the development of the slip-form paver, laying concrete required six different machines, each one with its own operator. The state of California has been a leader in slip-form paving. Machines used there are large enough to place three lanes—36 feet—of pavement in a single pass. Most machines pave only two lanes at a time.

An automatic paver is also used in laying asphalt. Steel wheel rollers compact the material once it has been spread. Some asphalt pavers are able to lay roadways 24 feet in width in a single pass, but most asphalt is laid in 12-foot widths.

Many sections of the Interstate Highway System have al-

Engineers call slip-form paving one of the greatest advances in highway construction in recent years.

ready been completed, and motorists reap great benefits from them. Much time is saved. In the city of Chicago, trips that used to take 40 minutes can now be made in one-quarter of that time. When the last link was recently completed in Route 75 in Michigan, it cut travel time between Sault Ste Marie and Detroit from ten hours to six hours.

Safety is another important factor. The Interstate System, by reducing traffic on nearby roads, helps to lower the number of accidents. The Bureau of Public Roads has estimated that when the Interstate System is completed it will save about 5,200 lives a year. Other estimates indicate that by the year 1980 the system will be saving 9,500 lives a year.

The Interstate System means savings in dollars too. The motorist finds his operating costs are reduced because he uses less fuel and oil. Tires don't wear out so quickly. Such savings are extremely important to companies in the trucking business.

What about highways of the future? By 1975, when the

population of the United States will have reached an estimated 237 million, there will be 117 million motor vehicles traveling 1.25 trillion miles a year. Some experts forecast that *another* 41,000 miles of highway will be required to handle the tremendous volume of traffic.

Highways of the future will last longer. They will be smoother, and they will be able to retain their smoothness for a longer period of time. They also will be better able to resist skids.

The asphalt industry believes that "thick lift" paving will be a common practice in the years to come. This means that the asphalt mix will be spread and packed in layers of up to 18 inches in depth. This lift will be topped by a skid-resistant asphalt surface.

Tomorrow's highway systems will be made safer by electronic controls. On today's expressways, the merging maneuver, whereby a car enters into the highway's traffic flow, is the major source of accidents. At present, pavement markings and the driver's judgment control merging. In the future electronic units will measure gaps in freeway traffic and advise motorists when it is safe to merge.

Once the motorist is safely on the expressway, another electronic system will guide him safely to his destination. Signs do this now, of course, but they don't do it very well. Surveys show that 15 per cent of all drivers on unfamiliar highways go past their exits. Using the electronic system, a driver will "tune in" a receiver in his automobile to his destination. At each interchange along the way, the receiver will pick up a coded signal which will instruct him as to the correct way to go.

Suppose a motorist's car breaks down? How can he summon help? This is a problem that has plagued highway engineers since the days of Henry Ford's Model-T. An electronic system has solved the problem. Other motorists, upon seeing a car in distress, will be able to flash their headlights into a trans-

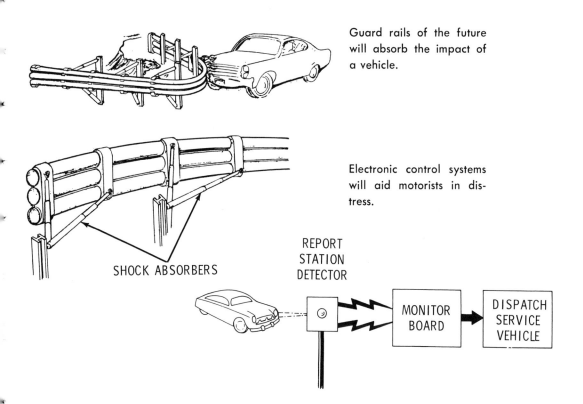

Guard rails of the future will absorb the impact of a vehicle.

Electronic control systems will aid motorists in distress.

SHOCK ABSORBERS

REPORT
STATION
DETECTOR

MONITOR BOARD

DISPATCH SERVICE VEHICLE

mitter which will, in turn, signal a central service location. Help will be dispatched immediately.

Other safety features of tomorrow's highways are likely to include sign supports and lamp posts of "breakaway" design. They yield under the impact of the vehicle that collides with them. Studies sponsored by the Texas State Highway Department have demonstrated the tremendous value of such construction in reducing the number of accident injuries and deaths. Barriers and guard rails of the future will be designed to absorb the impact of a vehicle instead of bouncing it back upon the roadway and into the path of oncoming cars.

Since horse-and-buggy days, right up to the present, a road has been little more than "a way of traveling between places"—to quote the dictionary. Thanks to advances in highway engineering, in the future it may be the *safer* way.

5 Steel in the Sky

In 1904 Othmar Hermann Ammann, a twenty-five-year-old civil engineer, sailed through The Narrows, the mile-and-one-quarter-wide entryway to New York Harbor, with visions of a career as a bridge builder.

Soon after his arrival Ammann found a job, stayed with it, and became one of the world's foremost designers of suspension bridges. He designed the George Washington Bridge across the Hudson River, which links New York and New Jersey, and the Bayonne Bridge, from Staten Island to Bayonne in New Jersey, the longest arch span bridge in the world. Ammann was also one of the three consulting engineer-advisers on the construction of San Francisco's famed Golden Gate Bridge. But the climax of his career was—quite fittingly—a bridge of spectacular size and beauty across The Narrows. Completed in 1964, it is a miracle of modern engineering.

"Everything about the Narrows bridge is big, bigger or biggest," reports an engineering magazine. It has the world's longest main suspension span—4,260 feet from tower to tower—which means that there is four-fifths of a mile of steel and concrete hanging in the air above the ship channel.

Each of the bridge's two towers is 693 feet high; the

Cable ends of the Verrazano-Narrows Bridge are imbedded in enormous steel-reinforced concrete anchorages.

foundations reach down 105 feet on one, and 170 feet on the other. The towers' "legs" are so huge that each could easily enclose the Washington Monument.

The four steel cables that pass over the towers, from which the roadway is suspended, are each three feet in diameter. Each one has the strength to lift a ship the size of the S.S. *United States.* The steel-reinforced concrete anchorages at each shore point, in which the cable ends are imbedded, are just as spectacular. One block weighs 410,000 tons, more than the weight of the Empire State Building.

The bridge has been named the Verrazano-Narrows Bridge in honor of Giovanni da Verrazano, the Italian explorer who discovered New York Harbor in 1524. Perhaps the "biggest" feature of the structure is its success. The number of cars using the bridge has far exceeded engineers' estimates. A lower deck to handle six additional lanes of traffic will be open in 1968, six years earlier than planned.

The Verrazano-Narrows Bridge is an important connection in the Maine to Florida highway system along the Atlantic Coast. No longer does the motorist have to contend with the traffic-clogged streets of New York City. Using the bridge, he simply bypasses them. An even more vital link is to be found slightly more than 300 miles to the south. It is the Chesapeake Bay Bridge Tunnel. Like the Verrazano-Narrows Bridge, it is an engineering wonder.

Chesapeake Bay is one of the world's largest harbors. Baltimore, long a major port, lies within it, as does Norfolk, the principal East Coast base of the United States Navy. Its mouth is 13 miles across and, until recently, the only way to get from one side to the other was by automobile ferry or by means of a roundabout highway route which added more than 100 miles to one's journey.

Neither a bridge nor a tunnel was the answer to the problem of providing a way across the harbor's mouth. The Navy would not allow a bridge. It feared that, in the event of war, the enemy would bomb the bridge, thus blockading the entrance to Norfolk. To tunnel such a distance would be much too expensive. A compromise was reached: the structure would be a combination of a bridge, tunnel, and trestled roadway.

The crossing starts at Norfolk with a 3½-mile section of beam-supported highway over shallow water. Then the motorist encounters the first of four man-made islands, and the roadway dips into a mile-long tunnel. The road climbs out onto another island and becomes a trestle again for almost four miles. It crosses a third island, descends into another mile-long tunnel and out onto a fourth island. More miles of trestled roadway and a high-level steel bridge complete the crossing.

The four islands that anchor the tunnel ends and link them to the roadway sections were not a gift of nature. Engineers, working in angry seas, 30 to 40 feet deep, had to build each one. They began by laying a huge ring of rocks on the bottom of the bay. Then the ring was filled with sand. When the top of the sand pile was halfway to the water's surface, a second ring of rock was built around its perimeter. Then more sand was poured inside. The process was repeated until the island was built up to its full height.

The first persons to make a complete crossing of the whole bridge-tunnel complex were two young engineers who hiked all the way. It took them six hours and three minutes. Passenger cars make the trip in 25 minutes, cutting at least an hour from the time it used to take by ferry.

The Chesapeake Bridge-Tunnel opened in 1964. It has triggered other projects of the same type. In 1966 civil engineers announced plans for a nine-mile tunnel-bridge-causeway that will connect Prince Edward Island, which lies off Canada's eastern shore, with the mainland. Ever since Prince

A view of the Chesapeake Bay Bridge-Tunnel. Man-made islands (foreground) link the tunnel ends with roadway sections.

Edward Island became a part of Canada in 1873, its chief contact with the continent has been by means of ferryboat. When this construction project is completed, the province will gain mainland status at last.

The use of the arch in bridge construction dates to the earliest of times. Engineers agree that arch bridges are their most dramatic when placed across rock gorges. Nature then provides the bridge's structural support. There can be no better example of this than the spectacular Glen Canyon Bridge which spans the Colorado River at Page, Arizona, near the Arizona-Utah border. It is the highest steel arch in the world, a breath-taking 700 feet above the river bed.

Just upstream from the bridge is the Glen Canyon Dam, one of the nation's major engineering works of recent years. It is one of a series of dams that harnesses the Colorado's flow for power and irrigation.

The Glen Canyon Bridge was an important factor in the construction of the dam. Before the crossing was built, it was 190 road miles from one canyon wall to the other. The bridge

The Glen Canyon Bridge in Page, Arizona, is one of the most spectacular of all arch spans.

A prefabricated steel bridge unit is hoisted into place.

thus ranks as one of the most notable engineering conveniences of all time.

From coast to coast, from border to border, new bridges are going up. The biggest of these include the Delaware Memorial Bridge, which spans the Delaware River between Philadelphia and Wilmington. It is a $70 million twin to a bridge already in use, and was completed in 1968.

Another new bridge is the Newport Bridge, a $45 million, two-mile suspension crossing between Jamesport and Newport, Rhode Island. It opened in 1968. In building the Newport Bridge, the wire strands for the cables were manufactured in the factory and then taken to the bridge site on reels. This technique represents a major step forward. Always in the past cables had to be "spun" wire-by-wire over the bridge towers, a costly and time-consuming operation.

45

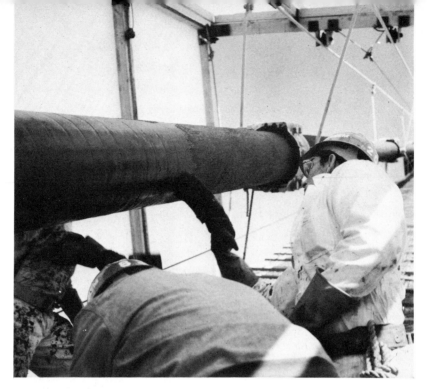
Suspension bridge cables get a protecting coat of liquid plastic.

The Newport Bridge saw another innovation. It had been customary to wrap and paint the bridge cables, once they were in place, to keep out dampness. But on the Newport span, the cables were coated with a thick plastic "syrup" which, when it hardened, gave perfect watertight protection.

On the West Coast, the largest new bridge is the $70 million structure across southern San Francisco Bay, the San Mateo-Hayward Bridge. It is 7.4 miles long, the world's longest "orthotropic" bridge. This is a type of bridge in which the flanged tops of the steel girders form the road deck. The girders are prefabricated and prepainted and then trucked to the site. A crane hoists each section into place. The deck plates do double duty. They give the bridge its structural support, and, after a thin coat of asphalt has been applied, serve as a roadway.

In 1968 the San Mateo-Hayward Bridge was voted the outstanding engineering achievement of the year by the American Society of Civil Engineers. No other bridge has ever been so honored.

6 Rapid Transit Renaissance

America is a car-happy nation. Every year more than eight million new cars are added to the approximately 100 million already on the roads. Highways are everywhere. They, and their rights of way, already cover 15 million acres, more than the whole state of West Virginia.

The situation is causing national concern. When a new freeway is built, thousands of homes are wiped out and families are uprooted. Peaceful countrysides are destroyed. Some people are afraid that the country may one day be paved coast to coast with concrete and asphalt. San Francisco, for example, has gone through a vigorous anti-freeway revolt. Recently the city voted down new freeways.

The country's love affair with the automobile has caused another problem: the traffic jam. In rush hours, freeways are not adequate. Cars can only inch along.

A case in point is the Long Island Expressway, a six-lane stretch of concrete, which starts in New York City and extends eastward 80 miles, cutting populated Long Island through the middle. In peak morning and evening periods, more than 60,000 vehicles use it. What happens enrages motorists. "Traffic moves so slowly," says one, "that you can drive to work and read the morning paper at the same time." A New York City daily newspaper calls the expressway "the world's longest parking lot."

One reason for the travail is that the Long Island Expressway must carry more than double the number of vehicles it was designed for. "Heaven only knows what we can do about it now," says New York City's traffic commissioner.

But cities all across the nation *are* doing something. In most cases, the solution lies with subways, buses, or trains—any form of rapid transit. Why rapid transit? This statistic provides the answer: A rapid transit route can carry as much as ten times the number of passengers as a freeway lane used by autos only.

Before World War II, only New York, Chicago, Boston, and Philadelphia, among North American cities, had major rail transit systems. Up until 1968, the only cities to add rapid transit in half a century were Cleveland, Montreal, and Toronto. But soon the list may be much longer. San Francisco is one name that will be added. In fact, San Francisco, drawing upon the talents of some of the best engineers in the country, is in

Completed tunnel for the San Francisco Bay Area system will provide rapid transit link between San Francisco and Oakland.

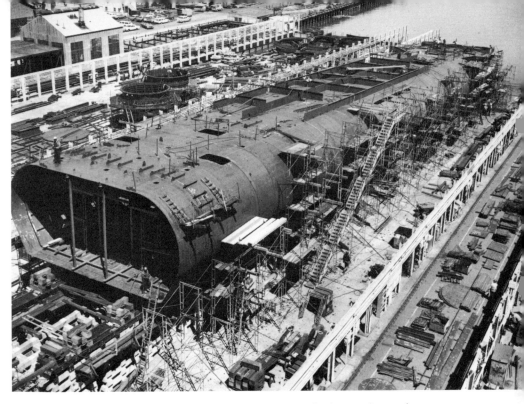

Tunnel sections for the Bay Area Rapid Transit System are built in a shipyard, then launched.

the midst of creating the first completely new rapid transit system in the United States in more than 40 years.

The San Francisco Bay Area Rapid Transit System is one of the largest construction projects under way in the world. When completed, $1.2 billion will have been spent. The job will employ 100 different contractors, 1,000 engineers, most of them civil engineers, and at the height of construction, more than 8,000 workmen. The system will link downtown San Francisco with the City of Oakland, and with Contra Costa and Alameda counties which lie to the east across San Francisco Bay. In total it will be 75 miles long, with about one-third of it underground. By the early 1970's, San Franciscans will be riding ultramodern, air-conditioned passenger cars which will average 50 mph, and will be capable of bursts of up to 80 mph. The entire system will be electronically controlled.

From an engineering standpoint, the most challenging phase

of the Bay Area transit system is the construction of the trans-bay tube. It will stretch like an enormous pipeline for a distance of 3.6 miles under the bay from San Francisco to Oakland in water that reaches a depth of 130 feet in places. It will be the longest and deepest underwater crossing in the world.

Sections of the tube are built in a shipyard. Each one is binocular-shaped, providing for two tracks, one in each direction. Made of steel, they average 330 feet in length, slightly longer than a football field. Fifty-seven of them are required.

As sections of the tunnel are being fabricated, other contractors are dredging a tremendous trench on the bottom of the bay into which the sections are to be placed. This ditch is 70 to 100 feet deep with sloping sides. A smooth bed of gravel, two feet thick, is placed in the bottom of the trench.

After a tube section is completed, it is launched and tugboats nudge it to a nearby pier. Concrete is poured into the tube to form the interior walls and the trackway. When this weight has been added, only 2½ feet of the tube shows above the water's surface. Then the tugs push the tube out into the bay. A floating rig, as long as a city block, is waiting. Called a placing barge, it is made up of two railroad barges tied together by a pair of heavy steel trusses. Space has been left between the barges to provide a "berth" for the floating tube section. A system of winches and cables lowers it into the trench.

When a tube section is in place above the trench, crushed rock and gravel are poured from the placing barge into steel boxes mounted on top of the section. This added ballast causes the tube to slip silently below the water's surface, stout steel cables keeping it level. Divers wait on the bottom to help guide it into place. The tube is brought into line about three feet from the section already in place. Then the rubber-rimmed ends of the two sections are drawn tightly together by means of four couplers, similar to the couplers that connect railroad cars. Sand and gravel are poured over the tube to lock it into the trench.

Later the bulkheads at each end are removed and permanent steel connections are welded into place. From start to finish, it's a delicate operation.

Passengers using the new system will get a luxury ride. Cars will boast picture windows, carpeting, and glare-free lighting. They will be a foot lower than most, and will ride on tracks that are 9½ inches wider than normal. These features will minimize the side-to-side sway common to most trains.

Automation will be a major feature of the system. A single electronic "brain" will control each train's speed and the amount of time spent at stations. "It will do the job much more efficiently than a human could," says one of the engineers who helped plan the system. "At rush hours, the automatic control system will direct the operation of more than 50 trains scattered over 75 miles of line, and at speeds of up to 80 mph. They will run close to 90 seconds apart.

"There will be an operator in each train. But his job will be to watch for obstructions on the track, announce stations on the train's intercom system, and answer passenger's questions. Passengers like to see an operator. It makes them feel secure."

The fare collection system will be automatic, too. Regular passengers will be issued a plastic credit card with an account number. Before boarding a train and again on exiting, a passen-

Tube sections are lowered carefully to the bay bottom.

Interiors of transit cars for Bay Area system provide the last word in comfort and convenience.

ger will insert the card into a special recording slot. Electronic equipment will compute his fare. Each month he gets a bill.

What San Francisco is doing will set the country's standards in the field of rapid transit for years to come. But other cities are not far behind. Construction on a 25-mile subway system for Washington, D.C., a $430 million project, began in 1968. The first sections will be opened in the early 1970's. Seattle, Atlanta, and Los Angeles are also planning subways.

Many American cities have been impressed by the new subway system in Montreal which opened in 1966. It has 15.9 miles of trackway and cost $214 million. Trains ride on rubber tires; it's quiet. About 50 per cent more people than expected are using the Montreal subway. Toronto is another Canadian city with a new and popular subway. It features cars of gleaming steel and aluminum, said to be the lightest and most economical to operate in North America.

The increased number of people in our nation, combined with the popularity of the automobile and decades of emphasis on highway construction, have endowed almost every American city with a severe transportation problem. But everywhere engineers have this problem under attack.

7 Water, Precious Water

We live in a thirsty world. The average person consumes the equivalent of 18 glasses of water a day. It takes 110,000 gallons of water to make a ton of steel. A ton of paper requires 184,000 gallons, and a ton of synthetic rubber needs 660,000 gallons. A jetliner uses 1,000 gallons in take-off. It takes 550,000 gallons to launch an intercontinental missile.

Luckily, we live in a watery world. Three-quarters of the earth's surface is covered with water. Yet there are shortages in many parts of the world. The problem is not in the amount of water, but in having it in the place we need it, at the time we need it, and with the required quality.

California is a state that has more than its share of water troubles. The city of Los Angeles has lived with a drought for more than two centuries. Its average rainfall each year is about 16 inches, one-third of the amount that New York City receives. But Californians in the northern part of the state must cope with floods and poor drainage. Both north and south must struggle with salt water that seeps in from the sea to ruin fresh

Workers concrete an aqueduct, part of California's State Water Project.

water supplies. And some of the state's rivers are polluted.

The water needs are great. California has a soaring population, booming industry, and a prosperous agricultural economy. But about 70 per cent of California's water is found in the northernmost one-third of the state, while most of the people—77 per cent of them—live in the southern two-thirds.

These facts would seem to indicate a distressing situation. But this isn't the case at all. The people of Los Angeles are washing their cars, watering their lawns, and filling their swimming pools—and doing all of these without the slightest worry. Their water supply is assured at least through the year 2000, because Los Angeles learned long ago to reach out for its water. Most of its supply now comes from the Owens River Valley, on the eastern slope of the Sierras, 250 miles to the north. The city also taps the Colorado River, on the California-Arizona border, 250 miles to the east.

This "reaching out" involved bold construction projects. But what California has planned for the future will dwarf anything that has been accomplished in the past. "Tremendous, just tremendous—that's the only way to describe it," says one engineer. California's amazing engineering venture, known as the State Water Project, has these features:

It is the largest single water development project in the

world to be financed at one time. Its cost is approximately $2 billion.

The project contains the highest dam in the United States and the highest earthfill dam in the world. Located at Oroville, the towering structure rises 770 feet.

Also at Oroville, the project will have the largest underground power plant in the nation. This plant, working with a companion plant downstream, will produce enough electricity for a city of one million people.

What the State Water Project will do is collect water in the High Sierras of northern California, and move it to the heavily populated areas of the south, a 700-mile journey in some cases. This is the same as if Jacksonville, Florida, reached out to Philadelphia for its water supply. But distance isn't the only thing. There are high mountains that stand as obstacles. En route south, the water must be lifted over the 3,500-foot Tehachapi range. Construction on the State Water Project began in 1961. The first water was delivered to southern California the same decade, but it will be 1980 before the project reaches completion.

The cornerstone of this network of pipelines, aqueducts, power stations, and reservoirs is the dam across the Feather River at Oroville. Engineers began by building diversion tunnels to turn aside the spirited flow of the Feather River. This gave them a dry river bed upon which the dam could be built. A concrete "core" for the dam was then poured.

The tremendous amount of material needed for fill was close at hand. A half century ago Oroville was the scene of extensive placer-mining operations for gold. Dredges plied the rivers and streams in the area, picking up and washing rock fragments in the stream beds and separating the gold. The gravely waste—called "tailings"—is what engineers used as dam fill.

About 5,000 acres of tailings were strewn about the Oroville area. A bucket-wheel excavator, an earth-digging machine as big as a house, was the key factor in putting the tailings to use. Whirling like a carnival Ferris wheel, the excavator's giant 30-foot digging wheel, fitted with eight steel-toothed steel buckets, ripped great scoops of tailings from where they lay, and tumbled them into a conveyer-belt system. The conveyer system fed a train of 40 gondola cars which carried the fill to the dam. Another belt system then distributed the material. Engineers say that the construction of the Oroville Dam was the largest earth-moving job that the world has ever known.

Modern engineering methods are often called upon to solve water problems. In Albuquerque, New Mexico, the supply of water from the Rio Grande River became insufficient as the city's population increased. Engineers decided to boost the flow by connecting the Rio Grande with the Colorado River. This required drilling a 12.8-mile tunnel through a sandstone ridge of the Rocky Mountains.

To perform this feat they called upon a little known but spectacular piece of equipment called a "mole." Cylinder-shaped, and as big as a railroad freight car, the mole braces itself against the tunnel wall with its eight hydraulic jacks. Then its many drilling heads go to work, chewing through the rock at the incredible speed of 200 feet a day. The operator rides in the rear in an air-conditioned cab.

Engineers have already begun to tap the world's most ample supply of water—the oceans. In the future, more and more Americans will be getting their water from the sea.

There is nothing really new about "desalinization," the process of removing salt from water. Julius Caesar converted salt water to fresh for his legions during the siege of Alexandria by distillation. The salt water is boiled into steam. The vapor, when cooled into liquid form, is pure water.

Only in the past few years, however, has desalinization been tried on a large scale. In the past, cost was a major problem. In 1953 it cost about $5 to convert 1,000 gallons of

Huge bucket-wheel excavator scoops up "tailings" to be used as fill in Oroville Dam across the Feather River.

Conveyor-belt systems like this one were vital to the construction of the Oroville Dam.

sea water into fresh, a price much too high for household or industrial use. But engineering and scientific advances have driven the cost downward. Large desalinization plants of the years just ahead will convert 1,000 gallons of sea water for about twenty cents.

Already costs are at a level which some city and industrial users are willing to pay. St. Thomas in the Virgin Islands used to pay $2 per 1,000 gallons for its water, which was brought by barge from Puerto Rico. A desalinization plant now produces fresh water for about half that amount.

The first large plant to make fresh water from salt water was built in Kuwait, a small, sun-baked, oil-rich country on the Persian Gulf, in 1948. Late in 1967, there were close to 100 such plants in operation around the world, from Aruba to Libya, from Somerset, Massachusetts, to Chocolate Bayou, Texas. One of the largest was opened in Key West, Florida, in 1967.

Key West is the principal city of the Florida Keys, a chain of tiny coral islands strewn southward from Miami for about 150 miles. Water troubles tormented Key West for years. The city tried bringing in water in barges. Residents collected rain water. Wells were dug. But these sources weren't enough. The United States Navy, which has an important base at Key West, built a 130-mile water pipeline to the mainland, but service often broke down. In 1967 the situation got worse. People were told they could not wash their cars or water their lawns. There was talk that water might be turned off completely at certain times. Yet all around there was water, billions and billions of gallons of it in the Atlantic Ocean.

The water problems of the Keys vanished when the water desalting plant began operation. Located on Stock Island, it produces 2.62 million gallons a day.

The Key West plant, and most of the others throughout the world, operate on two well-known principles. The first is that

The face of the "mole" showing clusters of circular bits.

This tunnel was bored by a "mole" at the rate of 200 feet a day.

This desalting plant ended Key West's water troubles.

steam from a vessel such as a tea kettle will condense on the top of the container as pure water. The second is that the lower the atmospheric pressure, the lower the temperature needed to boil water. It takes 212°F. to boil water at sea level. But at Pikes Peak, which is at 14,000 feet, water can be boiled at 185°F. because the atmospheric pressure is so much lower.

In a large-scale desalting operation, the sea water is heated and sprayed into a low pressure chamber. Part of the water vaporizes or "flashes" into steam. Then the steam is condensed into pure water. This process is repeated several times. One gallon of fresh water is produced from every three gallons of sea water.

Water desalting plants of the future will make today's operations seem small by comparison. By 1980 we will have nuclear-powered plants turning out billions of gallons of water daily. The first of these will be a huge installation under construction on a 40-acre man-made island off the coast of Southern California near Long Beach. It will be able to produce 150 million gallons of fresh water a day, more than 50 times as much as the Key West plant; more, in fact, than the combined production of all the world's existing desalting plants.

8 Airports for Jumbo Jets

"We have a nightmare situation coming," says an airport planner. "It's scary."

The problem has to do with the airplane. It's getting bigger and bigger. The conventional jet, the jumbo jet, and, eventually, the supersonic transport are due to put staggering demands on airport ground facilities.

Jumbo jets—planes like the Boeing 747—are capable of transporting 490 passengers, four and five times as many as conventional jet craft. They will be in full service in the mid-1970's. They have a bit more speed than the present jets, but not much more. Their huge size is what makes them different. They give passengers a feeling they are aboard an ocean liner, not an airplane.

In 1939 airlines in the United States carried 1,700,000 passengers for the year. In 1967 airlines transported more than that number each week, about 100 million passengers for the year. Experts predict that this figure will double by the year 1975 when jumbo jet service is widespread. In 1985, when supersonic craft are the order of the day, 500 million passengers will be transported.

These statistics spell crisis for almost every single airport in the country. "The real bottleneck in the jet age is not in the air but on the ground," says William Pereira, the planner for the Los Angeles Airport Commission. "We must break the ground barrier," he declares.

This situation is one that deeply concerns the civil engineer. It is he who bears the responsibility for the planning, design, construction, and operation of the nation's municipal and military airports.

New York City is making a desperate search for a site for a new airport. Locations fifty and more miles from the city are being appraised. Airport planners in Chicago are talking over the possibility of getting additional airport space by building on fill in Lake Michigan. This facility would be several miles out from shore and connected by tunnel to the mainland.

Dramatic airport plans are also being considered in Los Angeles. Five new airline terminals, all of them underground, are being planned. One of two methods will be used to get passengers to their planes, and each is as futuristic as commercial supersonic flight itself. One method is to have the passenger lounges rise from their subterranean terminals by means of great hydraulic jacks, unload passengers into the aircraft, and then sink back into the terminal. A second method would be to have huge enclosed escalators channel passengers from the underground lounges to the airplane's door.

That is what is to come. But the present is dramatic too. A growing number of the nation's airports, in terms of ground facilities, are ready now to receive the jumbo jets and supersonic craft. Notable examples of these are the new airport at Huntsville, Alabama, and the Metropolitan Airport of Sacramento which was completed late in 1967. But the nation's first and foremost super airport is Dulles International Airport,

Architect Eero Saarinen described the terminal building at Dulles International Airport as "a huge continuous hammock suspended between concrete trees."

located at Chantilly, Virginia, about forty minutes by automobile from Washington, D.C. Dulles International is the first commercial airport in the world to be planned from the start for today's jets and those to come.

To the eye, surely the most striking feature of Dulles International is its terminal building, an architectural triumph designed by the late Eero Saarinen. The structure rises dramatically, its curved roof high in front, lower in the middle, and slightly higher in the back. The roof is supported by cables— like those in a suspension bridge, but smaller—strung between columns on each side of the concourse. The columns are sloped outward to counteract the pull of the cables, but also to give the structure a dynamic and soaring look.

Before designing Dulles airport, a team of civil engineers, mechanical engineers, airport consultants, and architect Saarinen spent many months analyzing the whole problem of a

Passengers funnel from the mobile lounge into the aircraft.

large airport for jet craft. It sent out crews with counters and stop watches to find out what people really did at airports, how far they had to walk, and how long they had to wait in line. They investigated problems of flight schedules, aircraft taxiing, and baggage handling. Two conclusions were reached. First, passengers were already walking tremendous distances through terminal "fingers" leading to their planes. These distances would have to be increased in any terminal serving jumbo jets. Second, taxiing aircraft up to the terminal gate was found to be almost always very costly and inefficient.

A new method of passenger handling had to be found. The soundest thing to do was to bring the passengers to the plane, instead of following the traditional method of bringing the plane to the passengers. This they accomplished with a mobile lounge, a spacious room on wheels. It detaches from the terminal building and travels under its own power out to where the plane is parked.

The mobile lounge is as big as eight city buses. It accommodates 90 persons in air-conditioned comfort. Passengers using such a system are spared the long walk through finger extensions of the main terminal. They are protected from weather, noise, jet blasts, and fumes when entering or exiting from planes.

Three tremendous aircraft runways were built at Dulles, each about two miles in length. Made of a 15-inch layer of portland cement laid over a 9-inch base of crushed stone, the runways are strong enough to support aircraft weighing as much as half a million pounds. Enough concrete went into the runways to pave a two-lane highway stretching from New York City to Philadelphia, a distance of about 100 miles.

Many cities favor decentralized airport facilities; instead of having one air terminal, several "satellite" terminals are built, all serving and being served by the same aircraft runway system. Houston International Airport, the first stage of which opened in 1968, follows this theory. By 1975 the Houston airport will have four terminals plus a hotel complex. These facilities will be linked by an automated subway train. Called the

Many cities favor decentralized airport facilities. Instead of one air terminal, several "satellite" terminals are built.

In the future, travel between "downtown" and the airport may be by means of the rail-bus.

"Guide-O-Matic," it will transport passengers and their hand baggage to and from terminals to indoor parking lots. The trains will operate around the clock at two-minute intervals. There will be no motorman or conductor; a built-in guidance will keep the train on course.

Mid-Continent International Airport in Kansas City will tackle the problem of long walking distances another way, by building three huge circular terminals with parking space in the center of each. A passenger will drive to the terminal appropriate for his flight. The Dallas-Fort Worth Regional Airport is another that will feature a number of satellite terminals. They will be linked by a transportation "spine" containing roadways and an automated people-moving system.

The era of the jumbo jet is due to cause another headache —how to move the increased flow of people between the airport and the central city. Traffic jams are not uncommon on highways linking the two. They will become more frequent.

Dulles International Airport is serviced by a major expressway. The road is reserved for airport users exclusively over more than one-half its distance. Few airports are this fortunate. Other cities have considered monorail transportation, a single and elevated rail system with cars suspended from it. But transportation experts have turned thumbs down on the monorail. It carries too few passengers and requires the construction of a whole new trackage and terminal system.

In New York, Chicago, and Los Angeles, helicopters are being used to get passengers to airports. But helicopters are able to carry only a relatively few of the total number of persons using air transport. In New York City, the maximum number of passengers that can be carried by helicopter service in one hour is about 100. This number of people doesn't even begin to fill a jumbo jet.

There is a bright spot, however. It is a means of transportation that is capable of handling a significant number of people, is relatively inexpensive, does not have to travel on traffic-clogged highways, and is fast. It is the rail-bus.

The rail-bus picks up passengers at a downtown air terminal. Riding on conventional rubber tires, it travels to a nearby railroad crossing. There, at the flick of a switch, the rubber wheels are retracted and four steel rail wheels come down on the railroad track. The changeover takes about one minute. Near the airport, the rail-bus switches back to the highway. New York City has successfully tested the rail-bus. It may be one answer to the "get-me-to-the-airport-on-time" problem.

9 Construction Around the World

England is separated from France by a tantalizing 22 miles, and a tunnel beneath the English Channel to link the two countries has been an engineering dream for more than two centuries. Soon that dream may be a reality.

Yellowing records show that the idea of boring through the solid chalk which lies beneath the ocean bottom goes back to 1751, the year that the Amiens Academy in France awarded a prize for the best design for an England-to-France undersea passage. Between 1833 and 1869 plans for channel tunnels, to accommodate the horse-drawn carriages of the day, were about as common as buggy whips. The advent of railroads and the steam locomotive of the 1850's brought forth a whole new batch of tunnel plans suited to rail transportation.

Not until 1872 were any plans given serious consideration. That year a group of investors began raising the enormous amount of money required, hiring the engineers and ordering the construction materials. In 1878 work began. But then the British public grew fearful. They had disturbing visions of great armies of enemy invaders streaming through the passage to conquer their tiny island. So strong was this feeling that work was halted. And it was never resumed.

During the 1950's, with the countries in Europe more friendly than they had been in years, England and France began to talk about getting on with the tunnel job. Tests were made to determine which of the two tunnel systems was the most practical. One group of engineers favored the sunken tube method. First a trench would be dredged across the channel bed. Then long sections of tunnel would be lowered into the trench from platforms on the surface of the sea. The sections would be joined on the bottom and then covered with crushed stone and gravel. Other engineers preferred to tunnel through the clay and chalk. This bore would be about 160 feet beneath the channel bottom.

No matter what method is decided upon, the British tunnel entrance is expected to be near Folkestone. The French will enter their side not far from Calais. Work is expected to begin in the 1970's.

The tunnel will be about 32 miles in length, of which 22 miles will be under the sea. It will be the longest railroad and automobile tunnel in the world—by far! The longest rail tunnel at present is the famous Simplon Tunnel through the Alps which links Italy and Switzerland. It is a mere 12 miles long. The world's longest tunnel for automobiles is beneath Mont Blanc and connects France and Italy. It measures less than eight miles.

As the English Channel tunnel project suggests, the list of world-wide construction projects is an extremely impressive one. Words such as "biggest," "longest," "widest," or "costliest" are needed to describe them. The Aswan High Dam is a case in point.

Aswan is in Egypt (the official name of the country is the United Arab Republic) and construction on the dam began in

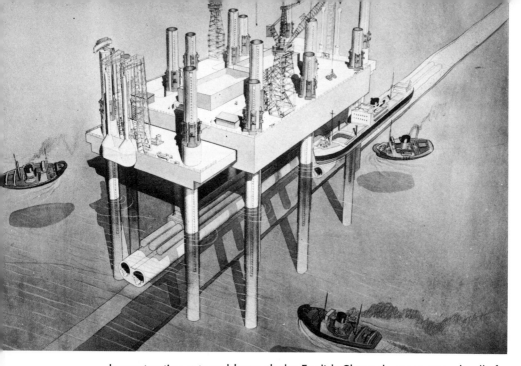

In constructing a tunnel beneath the English Channel, one proposal calls for the use of a huge platform from which tunnel sections could be lowered to the sea bottom.

1960. At one time more than 9,000 workers labored on the project, largely Egyptians, of course, but under the direction of Russian technicians and engineers. The first turbines began churning out electricity in 1967. The project was completed not long after, much sooner than 1970, as had been planned. It doubled the power output of the country.

By every manner of measurement, the dam at Aswan is a gigantic project. One engineer calls it a "modern colossus of the Nile." Indeed it is. Its cost is $1 billion, a colossal figure by any country's standards. It is 365 feet high; its crest is three miles long, and it is an incredible half a mile wide at its base. The largest rockfill dam in the world, it has the bulk of 17 pyramids the size of Egypt's largest, the Great Pyramid of Cheops at Giza. Lake Nasser, the name given the reservoir now forming in back of the dam, will be the largest man-made lake in the world, stretching 400 miles to the south, deep into the neighboring country of Sudan.

70

In the Netherlands, too, engineers are at work on a construction project that has a $1 billion price tag. This is not for one dam, however, but for several of them. The Dutch call the project the Delta Plan; it is the most ambitious and costly effort ever made to hold back the sea.

The project is focused on the southwestern part of the Netherlands. Here, six wide arms of the North Sea plunge far inland between wet mud flats and are fed by huge rivers—the Maas, Rhine, and Schledt. The Delta Plan will close off four of these funnel-shaped sea arms with massive dams at their mouths. Two will be left open to permit sea traffic to reach the ports of Antwerp and Rotterdam.

The Dutch began to draw up the Delta Plan in 1952. Work began in 1956. It has been continuing steadily since, and will probably be completed in 1978.

Closing the sea arms, which requires dams that are from two to five miles long, is a tricky and dangerous piece of business. The powerful flow of river water presses from one side, and menacing tidal currents from the other. The first step is to unroll nylon carpeting along the sea bed to keep the sandy bottom from shifting. The carpet is fitted with pockets which are filled with sand to hold it in place. Then sand and rubble are dumped on top. The final closing of the gap is achieved by floating metal watertight boxes, called "caissons," into place and sinking them.

Besides providing flood protection and control, the Delta Plan will keep the sea water out of the rivers and thereby check soil saltiness which ruins farmland. It will also provide new land for farming. Though the Delta Plan is a twenty-year project, and its cost a heavy burden upon the Dutch, they bear it with pleasure. When it is completed they will have conquered their age-old enemy, the sea.

Australia is another country where a construction program of great national importance is under way. It is the driest of all continents, averaging only 16 inches of rainfall a year, about the same as such "dry" American cities as Tucson, Arizona, and Salt Lake City, Utah. There is little water in Australia to generate electric power or irrigate thirsty farmlands.

To help correct this situation, Australians have launched the Snowy Mountain Project. The Snowys, located in the southeast corner of the country, are Australia's only mountain range. They boast several big, swift-flowing rivers, fine for making electric power. But the rivers run the "wrong" way, racing eastward to be lost in the sea. With huge dams and long tunnels through the mountains, engineers are seeking to corral these rivers and turn them around so that they flow westward to irrigate dry inland areas. In the process, the waters will be diverted through power stations to produce electricity.

The Snowy Mountain Project was begun in 1949 and is scheduled for completion in the 1970's. It involves the construction of 17 large dams and many smaller ones, nine power stations, and nearly 100 miles of tunnels. It is the largest con-

Dutch tugs nudge floating "caissons" into place to complete the closing of an arm of the sea.

Hundreds of visitors are on hand for official opening of Tumut Pond Dam, part of Australia's Snowy Mountain Project.

struction job ever attempted in Australia, and has been named one of the seven civil engineering wonders of the modern world. Every Australian speaks of the project with pride, and it is justifiable.

These are only a sampling of the world-wide construction projects. There are countless others. Portuguese engineers recently completed the Tagus River Bridge at Lisbon. With a total length of two miles, it is the longest suspension bridge in Europe. Buenos Aires now has a 60-story office and apartment building, the highest structure in South America. Italy is spending half a billion dollars on a gigantic road-building project. Japan is embarked on a vast expansion of thermal power output. Switzerland is planning the world's highest dam. Tunnels, dams, bridges, buildings—the whole world hums with construction activity.

10 Space-age Engineering

Will America be the first to reach the moon?

To a great extent the answer depends upon the civil engineer, upon his skill in constructing the earth-bound facilities required for the moon mission. James Webb, Administrator of the National Aeronautics and Space Administration (NASA), puts it this way: "The road to the moon is paved with brick, steel, and concrete put in place here on earth."

As a launch vehicle, the moon mission will use the enormous power of the Saturn V. This will propel the three-man Apollo spacecraft in which astronauts will travel to the moon.

The United States hopes to land an astronaut on the moon by 1970. Launch facilities are located on Merritt Island adjacent to Cape Kennedy, a sandy spot of land that juts into the Atlantic Ocean on the east coast of central Florida. Here, engineers recently completed the construction of Launch Complex 39. It is the "brick, steel, and concrete" that will put Americans on the moon.

The Vehicle Assembly Building (VAB), a massive concrete

box sheathed in aluminum, is the hub of the operation. Never before has man built a building so huge. The largest structures of recent times are the Pentagon Building in Washington and the Merchandise Mart in Chicago. The Vehicle Assembly Building is almost big enough to house them both.

Operations in the building begin when parts of the Saturn V rocket and the Apollo spacecraft arrive from test sites in various parts of the country. They are assembled and checked out in the "high bay area," the heart of the VAB. This is the biggest room in the world. Its doors are 456 feet tall. Technicians on tiered platforms, which can be retracted automatically, work on all levels of the rocket. When assembly is complete and the Saturn V-Apollo has passed its check-out tests, the immense doors of the building part to permit the crawler-transporter to enter and carry the space vehicle to the launch site. These doors are so huge that they could easily admit the United Nations secretariat building.

The crawler-transporter slips under the mobile launcher, and raises the launch platform and tower with the rocket and

The crawler-transporter, the vehicle used to carry the space vehicle and the mobile launcher to the launch site.

spacecraft into carrying position. It is a 12-million-pound load! Then the crawler-transporter carries its great cargo over the crawlerway, a three-and-one-half mile strip of roadway wider than the New Jersey Turnpike, to one of two launch pads. It travels on four double-tracked crawlers. Each is 10 feet high and 40 feet long. As one would expect, the transporter travels at a snail's pace—about one mile an hour.

The launch pad is a mound of earth and reinforced concrete 48 feet high. It covers an area the size of three football fields. Here the transporter sets down the mobile launch platform and the flight-ready space vehicle. A hydrogen service tower, a fuel system service tower, and an electrical power pedestal stand ready to inject life and lift into the rocket. The mobile launcher is secured to various mechanical systems on the pad. Then the crawler-transporter backs away, to return later with the mobile service structure. A derrick-type tower, it has five circular work platforms that close about the space vehicle. It is removed from the pad before launch.

The launch control center, a four-story building, is the electronic brain of Launch Complex 39. Here is where the final tests and check-outs take place. Here is where the countdown is conducted.

At other sites on Cape Kennedy, smaller rockets are assembled and tested right on the launching pad. But this presents difficulties. Bad weather often interferes with work. Weeks of delay result. At Launch Complex 39, technicians can set up and fire in a matter of days.

Constructing earth-bound launch facilities is only half the story. "Let's not forget there must also be a station at the other end," says William H. Wisely, Executive Secretary of the American Society of Civil Engineers. "Some brick, concrete, and steel—or their equivalents on the moon—will have to be put in place there too!"

Today we know a great deal more about the moon than we

The "high bay area" of the Vehicle Assembly Building.

Towering doors of the VAB part to allow the space vehicle and the mobile launcher to exit.

An aerial view of the five-acre lunar terrain that engineers have built near Calverton, New York.

did a decade ago. In years past our knowledge was based almost entirely on observations made by telescope or radar. During the late 1960's, spacecraft that orbited the moon and probed its surface sent back outstanding photographs which increased our knowledge immensely.

Using this information, as well as data obtained from earthbound photometric instruments, soil engineers have created a five-acre moonscape here on earth. This piece of simulated lunar terrain is made of fly ash, cinders, and porous furnace slag, and is located on Long Island near the town of Calverton, about 75 miles east of New York City. Using this site, engineers have been able to test vehicles to be used for housing and movement on the moon, as well as other pieces of equipment. "The lunar site is preparing us to cope with the intricacies of a new terrain," says one engineer. "It's here we're doing our homework."

Terrain is only one of the problems that moon exploration and colonization present. There are many others. But engineers are confident that they can be solved.

The moon is seemingly without air or water. Its surface is bombarded by micrometeorites, ultraviolet rays, and cosmic rays. Temperatures range from 200 degrees below zero to 200 degrees above. The first moon visitors will have to bring their air and water with them, as well as protective covering for the harsh environment. Sanitary engineering will be of critical importance. An energy source will be needed. Perhaps nuclear power or solar batteries will be the answer.

Later, lunar colonies will be constructed. They may be underground shelters carved out of the moon's surface. But the difference in gravity will make building conditions that engineers have never experienced yet. And the colonies will have to be self-supporting—oxygen, water, food, fuel, power.

Scientists say that moon exploration and colonization are just the beginning. From the moon, men will strike out to explore the farthest reaches of space, an adventure that presents a sharp challenge to the construction engineers of the future.

INDEX